Wave
Rebel

JIM DAVIS

RAVETTE PUBLISHING

First published by
Ravette Publishing Limited 1995

Printed and bound in Great Britain
for Ravette Publishing Limited,
Unit 3, Tristar Centre,
Star Road, Partridge Green,
West Sussex RH13 8RA
by Cox & Wyman Ltd, Reading, Berkshire.

ISBN: 1 85304 317 6

© 1993 United Feature Syndicate, Inc.

© 1993 United Feature Syndicate, Inc.

© 1993 United Feature Syndicate, Inc.

© 1993 United Feature Syndicate, Inc.

© 1993 United Feature Syndicate, Inc.

© 1993 United Feature Syndicate, Inc.

HOW COME **YOU** ALWAYS GET TO PICK WHAT WE DO?

BECAUSE **YOU** CAN NEVER THINK OF ANYTHING, THAT'S WHY

© 1993 United Feature Syndicate, Inc.

JIM DAVIS 11-6

© 1993 United Feature Syndicate, Inc.

© 1993 United Feature Syndicate, Inc.

SOMETHING VERY TRAGIC JUST HAPPENED TO ODIE!

© 1993 United Feature Syndicate, Inc.

JIM DAVIS 11-27

© 1993 United Feature Syndicate, Inc.

© 1993 United Feature Syndicate, Inc.

© 1993 United Feature Syndicate, Inc.

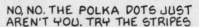

© 1993 United Feature Syndicate, Inc.

JIM DAVIS 1-3-94

© 1993 United Feature Syndicate, Inc.

© 1993 United Feature Syndicate, Inc.

© 1994 United Feature Syndicate, Inc

© 1994 United Feature Syndicate, Inc

© 1994 United Feature Syndicate, Inc.

JIM DAVIS 1-22

JIM DAVIS 1-31

© 1994 United Feature Syndicate Inc

THE BANK'S SECURITY CAMERA TOOK THIS PICTURE OF THE CULPRIT

JIM DAVIS 2-4

© 1994 United Feature Syndicate Inc.

I THOUGHT IT WAS A BAKERY!

© 1994 United Feature Syndicate Inc

THAT'S ENOUGH
OF THAT

© 1994 United Feature Syndicate, Inc.

UH, I'M NOT THERE
ANYMORE, ODIE

JIM DAVIS 29

© 1994 United Feature Syndicate Inc.

© 1994 United Feature Syndicate, Inc.

© 1994 United Feature Syndicate, Inc.

© 1994 United Feature Syndicate, Inc.

© 1994 United Feature Syndicate, Inc.

© 1994 United Feature Syndicate, Inc.

OTHER GARFIELD BOOKS IN THIS SERIES

COLOUR TV SPECIALS

Here Comes Garfield	£2.95
Garfield On The Town	£2.95
Garfield In The Rough	£2.95
Garfield In Disguise	£2.95
Garfield In Paradise	£2.95
Garfield Goes To Hollywood	£2.95
A Garfield Christmas	£3.99
Garfield's Thanksgiving	£2.95
Garfield's Feline Fantasies	£2.95
Garfield Gets A Life	£2.95

GARFIELD GALLERIES

Gallery 1	£2.99
Gallery 2	£2.99
Gallery 3	£2.99
Gallery 5	£2.99
Gallery 7	£2.99

All Ravette books are available at your local bookshop or from the address below. Just tick the titles required and send the form with your remittance to:-

B.B.C.S., P.O. BOX 941, HULL, NORTH HUMBERSIDE HU1 3YQ
24 Hour Telephone Credit Card Line 01482 224626
Prices and availability are subject to change without notice.

Please enclose a cheque or postal order made payable to B.B.C.S. to the value of the cover price of the book and allow the following for postage and packing:

U.K. & B.F.P.O: £1.00 for the first book and 50p for each additional book to a maximum of £3.50.

Overseas & Eire: £2.00 for the first book, £1.00 for the second and 50p for each additional book.

BLOCK CAPITALS PLEASE

Name ....

Address ....

....

....

Cards accepted: Mastercard and Visa

Expiry Date........................... Signature..